GW01044251

Key Stage 2
National Tests

English

Practice Papers

English

Key Stage 2

Practice Papers

Sch

For school and home
■
Based on the
Primary Framework
for literacy

Introduction

This book contains four practice papers. They will test your skills in reading and writing. Use them to practise for the English tests at the end of Year 6.

How to use the English Key Stage 2 Practice Papers

Decide when you are going to take one of the practice papers. Ask an adult to keep that time free to help you. **Do not look at any of the papers before then.**

What you will need

Equipment:

- a pen or pencil and a rubber
- lined paper for the Writing Test *Longer Task*
- a clock or watch (the Reading Test and the Writing Test *Longer Task* and *Shorter Task* are timed).

Adult help:

- to make sure that you spend the right amount of time on each test (in the test instructions, the clock symbol shows when timing should begin)
- to read aloud the Writing Test *Longer Task: Instructions and Planning*, and the Writing Test *Shorter Task* and Spelling Test
- to mark each test when you have finished it.

Before you start

Read through the general instructions on page 5. You will have more detailed instructions when you are ready to begin. Make sure that you have an adult with you when you are ready to start one of the papers.

After taking the practice papers

- Ask an adult to mark your practice papers (using the answers on pages 24 to 34). When you have the total scores, you or the adult should write them in the boxes on page 3 (opposite).
- If there were some questions that you couldn't do, don't worry – the Schofield & Sims Revision Guide will help! You can buy this separately. At the bottom of most of the practice paper pages, or in the answer pages, you will find some Revision Guide page numbers. Use these pages to revise the topics after you have done the papers.

Published by Schofield and Sims Ltd,
Dogley Mill, Fenay Bridge, Huddersfield HD8 0NQ, UK
Tel 01484 607080
www.schofieldandsims.co.uk

First published in 2004
Eighth impression 2010
Copyright © Schofield and Sims Ltd 2004

Author: Carol Matchett
Carol Matchett has asserted her moral right under the Copyright, Designs and Patents Act, 1988, to be identified as the author of this work.

The extract from the story **Camilla** *(contained within the pull-out Reading Booklet, pages 3 to 7) is by Adèle Geras, and is taken from the Oxford Book of Scary Tales (Oxford University Press, 1992).* **Camilla** *is copyright © Adèle Geras 1991. Permission granted by the Author.*

British Library Cataloguing in Publication Data
A catalogue record for this book is available from the British Library.

*Edited by Carolyn Richardson Publishing Services
(cr@publiserve.co.uk)*

Designed by Oxford Designers & Illustrators

Printed in the UK by Wyndeham Gait Ltd, Grimsby.

ISBN 978 07217 0956 7

English
Key Stage 2 Practice Papers
Carol Matchett

Write your name and school below before you start using this book.

First Name	
Last Name	
School	

Summary of practice paper scores

After you have finished each test and had it marked, write your test scores in these boxes.

Reading Test	
Writing Test *Longer Task: Instructions and Planning*	
Writing Test *Shorter Task*	
Spelling Test	
Total	

Note for teachers and parents

The Schofield & Sims Practice Papers have been written by teachers, for use at school and at home. Both design and content are similar to the National Curriculum Key Stage tests (SATs) used in schools. You can ensure that the practice papers are used properly by reading the introduction (page 2) and the instructions on pages 5, 6 and 17. Help the child by reading aloud the Writing and Spelling Tests, by timing the test sessions and by marking the completed papers (full instructions and mark schemes are supplied). You can get an idea of the educational level at which the child is working using the charts on page 35. The separate Revision Guide (cross-referenced at the foot of each practice paper page, or in the answer pages) enables children to revise independently for the tests: see back cover for full details.

Schofield&Sims

Contents

As explained in the Introduction, there are four practice papers in this book. One of them is a Reading Test. The other three are Writing Test papers (the *Longer Task: Instructions and Planning*, the *Shorter Task* and the Spelling Test). All four tests are described on page 5 (opposite).

These are the parts of the book that you will need to use as you work through the practice papers:

This is a pull-out booklet that you will need to use in the Reading Test. Ask an adult to pull it out from the centre of this book just before you start the test. It begins after page 18.

The book also contains the following pages, which are best used by an adult:

This page needs to be cut out from the book by an adult, just before the Spelling Test begins.

General instructions

Instructions

- It is best to do the papers in the same order as they appear in the book. The Reading Test comes first.
- 🕐 **Apart from the Spelling Test, all the tests in this book are timed**.
- Work as quickly and as carefully as you can.
- If you cannot do a question, go on to the next one. If you have time, you can come back to it later.
- If you finish before the end, go back and check your work.
- Follow the instructions for each question carefully. Some general instructions are given below. You will have more detailed instructions to read just before you take the test.

Reading Test

You are asked to read the Reading Booklet *Explaining the Unexplained?* and then to answer questions about it. The Reading Booklet is a pull-out booklet. You should ask an adult to pull it out of the centre of this book just before you start the test. You have 45 minutes to do the Reading Test, which is in the main Practice Papers book. The space for each answer shows you what type of writing is needed. Read the instructions carefully so that you know how to answer.

Writing Test *Longer Task: Instructions and Planning*

You are given some ideas that will help you to do a long piece of writing. The adult who is helping you will read aloud these ideas with you. You then have 45 minutes to do the writing. Allow up to 10 minutes of this time for planning your writing. **You will need lined paper to write on.**

Writing Test *Shorter Task*

For the Writing Test *Shorter Task* you are given some ideas that will help you to do a shorter piece of writing. The adult who is helping you will read aloud these ideas with you. You then have 20 minutes to do the writing. You write on the sheet that is provided.

Spelling Test

For the Spelling Test the adult who is helping you will read out a passage of text to you. You will have the same piece of text in front of you, but some words will be missing. You have to write the missing words in the gaps. Listen carefully when the adult reads out each word, and do your best to spell it correctly.

Remember

- **Don't cheat by reading the questions before the test, or by looking at the answers. If you do, your score won't be accurate.**
- **During the tests, think about each question carefully and try your best to answer it.**

**DO NOT TURN OVER THIS PAGE UNTIL YOU ARE READY TO
START THE READING TEST.**

Instructions for the Reading Test

There are two parts to the Reading Test materials:

	Pages
● The 12-page pull-out **Reading Booklet**, *Explaining the Unexplained?* Just before the test, ask an adult to pull the booklet out from the centre of this book. It begins after page 18.	(Pull-out pages 1–12)
● The **Reading Test**, which contains the test questions. Below each question, there is space for you to answer.	7–16

Do not look at the Reading Booklet or the Reading Test before you start the test.

You will have 15 minutes to read the Reading Booklet, *Explaining the Unexplained?* Ask someone to time this for you.

You should not begin to answer the questions during this time. Do not worry if you have not finished reading everything at the end of 15 minutes. You will be able to look at the Reading Booklet while you are answering the questions.

Before you begin answering the questions, read the information below about different types of questions and answers.

After 15 minutes of reading the Reading Booklet, you should begin the Reading Test. When you are ready to start the test, turn to the first question on page 7. Start timing the 45 minutes at this point.

Work through the pages, answering the questions as you go. Stop at the end of page 16. The end of the test is clearly marked.

Answering the different types of question

On pages 7 to 16 you will find different types of question.

● **Questions needing a short answer** Some questions will give you a short line for the answer. This shows that you only need to write a word or a phrase.

● **Questions needing a sentence or two** Some questions are followed by two or three lines. This shows that you need to write a sentence or two for your answer.

● **Questions needing longer answers** Some questions are followed by a large box or a greater number of lines. Here, you need to give a longer and more detailed answer.

● **Other types of answer** Some questions ask you to tick or circle your answer, or to put numbers in a box. Read the instructions so that you know how to answer.

Marks

The numbers in the right-hand margin tell you how many marks each question is worth.

**REMEMBER, YOU HAVE 45 MINUTES TO ANSWER THE QUESTIONS.
USE THE READING BOOKLET TO HELP YOU ANSWER THEM.**

Reading Test

SECTION 1

> **Look at the Reading Booklet *Explaining the Unexplained?*
> These questions are about the story *Camilla* (pages 3 to 7).**

Choose the best word or group of words to complete these sentences about the story.

Put a *ring* around your choice.

1.   The name of the interviewer was

| Monica Bridges. | Lynn Michael. | Mrs Ashton. | Camilla. |

1 mark

2.   The events described in the interview happened

| recently. | less than 40 years ago. | over 40 years ago. | when Lynn Michael was ten. |

1 mark

3.   The fancy dress party was held on a

| Friday evening. | Sunday afternoon. | school day. | Saturday. |

1 mark

4.   Monica Bridges describes her friend Sarah as her *bread-and-butter sort of friend*. What does this tell us about their friendship?

_____

_____

1 mark

please turn over

Schofield&Sims
English Key Stage 2
Practice Papers

> **Revision Guide links**
> If you need help after your test has been marked, read the following pages in the Revision Guide:
> **Question 4**: pages 10, 11

5. Monica was desperate to have Camilla as her best friend. What was it about Camilla that attracted her? Give **two** reasons.

_____

_____

_____

_____

_____

6. After Monica Bridges first mentions Camilla there is a long silence on the tape before she continues. Why do you think she pauses at this point?

_____

_____

_____

7. These are some of the main events in the story.

    Number them to show the sequence of events. The first one has already been done for you.

    [ ] Camilla gives Monica her bracelet.

    [ ] Camilla says she will not be able to come to Monica's party.

    [ ] Monica shows Lynn Michael a bracelet engraved with the name Camilla.

    [ ] Mrs Ashton tells the class about Camilla's death.

    [1] Monica wants Camilla to be her best friend.

Revision Guide links
If you need help after your test has been marked, read the following pages in the Revision Guide:
Question 5: page 6; **Question 6**: page 7; **Question 7**: page 5

8. Look at the story as far as Mrs Ashton's announcement on page 6.
    How does the author build up the feeling that something strange has
    happened to Camilla? Refer to events **before**, **during** and **after** the party.

    _____

    _____

    _____

    _____

    _____

                                                                            3 marks

9. Explain fully how you think Monica feels when Mrs Ashton tells
    them the news of Camilla's death?

    _____

    _____

    _____

    _____

                                                                            1 mark

10. In the interview Monica Bridges says:

    *Maybe what happened all those years ago has turned me into the
    kind of writer I am.* (page 3)

    Explain what she means by this.

    _____

    _____

    _____

                                                                            1 mark

Schofield&Sims
English Key Stage 2
Practice Papers

Revision Guide links
If you need help after your test has been marked, read the following pages in the Revision Guide:
Question 8: page 8; **Question 9**: page 7; **Question 10**: page 13

11.   The story of Camilla is told from whose point of view?

      Tick **one** answer.

      From Camilla's point of view. ☐

      From Lynn Michael's point of view. ☐

      From Monica Bridges' point of view. ☐

      From a third person narrator's point of view. ☐

12.   The story *Camilla* might be described as a ghost story.

      How is the story different to a typical ghost story?

      Give **three** differences.

      • _____

      • _____

      • _____

13.   Did you enjoy reading this story?

      Tick **one** answer.

      Yes ☐   No ☐

      Explain your opinion as fully as you can, referring to different aspects of the story.

      _____

      _____

      _____

      _____

      _____

Revision Guide links
If you need help after your test has been marked, read the following pages in the Revision Guide:
Question 11: page 9; **Question 12**: page 12; **Question 13**: page 15

SECTION 2

> **These questions are about the poem 'Ruins'**
> **(Reading Booklet page 8)**

14.   This poem is about the poet's visit to the ruins of a castle.

Find **two** words or phrases that suggest what the weather was like on the day of the visit.

Write one word or phrase next to each dot.

●   _____

●   _____

1 mark

15.   The poem is in two parts. How are the two parts different?

Think about the main ideas in each part of the poem and the way the lines are written.

a)   the main ideas   _____

_____

1 mark

b)   the way the lines are written   _____

_____

1 mark

16.   *Jagged walls with eyeless openings* (line 2)

a)   What are the *eyeless openings*?   _____

1 mark

b)   Why does the poet describe them in this way?   _____

_____

_____

1 mark

please turn over

Revision Guide links
If you need help after your test has been marked, read the following pages in the Revision Guide:
Question 14: page 17; **Question 15**: pages 16 and 21; **Question 16**: pages 18–19

SECTION 3

These questions are about the information
***Ghosts – fact or fiction?* (Reading Booklet pages 9 to 11).**

17. On page 9 the writer introduces the idea that some people believe in ghosts while others do not.

Write down one reason why people do believe in ghosts and another reason why they do not.

Why people do believe in ghosts:

_____

Why people do not believe in ghosts:

_____

18. Read the information about Rockenham Tower on page 9.

What is the purpose of this information?

Tick **one** answer.

to inform the reader ☐

to instruct the reader ☐

to persuade the reader ☐

to tell a story ☐

19. How does the writer build up the reader's interest in Rockenham Tower?

Give **two** ways.

_____

_____

Revision Guide links
If you need help after your test has been marked, read the following pages in the Revision Guide:
Question 17: page 24; **Question 18**: page 27; **Question 19**: page 32

20.   On page 10 (*Exploring the evidence*), the writer has used sub-headings.

Why has the writer used these when setting out the information?

_____

_____

1 mark

21.   Use some of the information from page 10 to help you complete this table of facts about ghosts. One whole section has been completed for you.

Where?	Evidence	Who?
The White House		
The George and Dragon Inn, Chester		
Raynham Hall, Norfolk	Photographed	The Brown Lady
		Admiral Sir George Tryon

3 marks

22.   On page 10 the writer gives five examples of ghosts. Only **one** of these sounds as though it might be dangerous. Which one?

Give a reason for your answer.

Choice: [   ]

Reason: _____

1 mark

_____

1 mark

please turn over

page 13 total

Schofield&Sims
English Key Stage 2
Practice Papers

Revision Guide links
If you need help after your test has been marked, read the following pages in the Revision Guide:
Question 20: page 28; **Question 21**: page 25; **Question 22**: page 26

23. On page 11 (*What do scientists say?*) the word ghosts usually appears in speech marks like this: '*ghosts*'

Why do you think the writer has done this?

_____

_____

_____ 1

24. Look at how the author has set out the scientific explanations on page 11.

Why has this layout been chosen?

_____

_____

_____ 1

25. Which of the scientific explanations might be used to explain the ghost at the George and Dragon Inn, Chester (page 10)?

Explain your choice fully.

_____

_____

_____ 2 m

26. The writer ends the article with three questions.

Why do you think the writer chose to end the article in this way?

_____

_____

_____ 1 r

Revision Guide links
If you need help after your test has been marked, read the following pages in the Revision Guide:
Question 23: page 22; **Question 24**: page 28; **Question 25**: page 26; **Question 26**: page 32

27.

> F.D. Roosevelt once said:
>
> I think it is unwise to say you
> do not believe in anything
> when you can't prove that it
> is either true or untrue.

Why do you think the writer chose to include this quotation?

_____

_____

_____

_____

1 mark

28.   After reading **all** the article on pages 9 to 11, which of these statements do
      you think best describes the author's point of view? Tick **one** box.

Ghosts definitely do exist.   ☐

There is definitely no such thing as a ghost.   ☐

We do not know for certain if ghosts exist.   ☐

1 mark

Explain your choice fully, referring to all parts of the article.

_____

_____

_____

_____

2 marks

please turn over

page 15
total

Revision Guide links
If you need help after your test has been marked, read the following pages in the Revision Guide:
Question 27: page 31; **Question 28**: page 30

SECTION 4

> **These questions are about the whole Reading Booklet.**

29. Compare the events in the story *Camilla* with the information given about the ghost of Admiral Sir George Tryon on page 10.

    Find **two** ways in which the events were similar.

    1. _____

    2. _____   **2 mar**

30. The title of the reading booklet is *Explaining the Unexplained?*

    Think about the story and the information given in the booklet and explain why you think this title was chosen.

    _____

    _____

    _____

    _____

    _____

    _____   **2 ma**

  page
  tot

> **This is the end of the Reading Test.**

**Reading Test
total score**
Write this score
in the box on
page 3

Revision Guide links
If you need help after your test has been marked, read the following pages in the Revision Guide:
Question 29: page 26; **Question 30**: page 13

Instructions for the Writing Test

There are three parts to the Writing Test:

	Pages
Longer Task You will have 45 minutes to complete your longer piece of writing.	18–19
Shorter Task You will have 20 minutes for the shorter piece of writing.	20–21
Spelling Test	22–23

Instructions for the *Longer Task*

Before you start, make sure that you have some lined paper to write on.
An adult will help you to read the ideas that are given on page 18.
Once you have read the task, start your planning, using page 19.
At this point, ask the adult helping you to start timing 45 minutes.
After 10 minutes you must start your writing. You can start earlier if you have finished your planning before this.
Ask the adult to remind you when there is 15 minutes of writing time left.

Instructions for the *Shorter Task*

An adult will help you to read the *Shorter Task* on page 20.
There is space on page 21 to write your answer, so you do not need any paper.
Once you have read the task, start your writing on page 21.
At this point, ask the adult helping you to start timing 20 minutes.
You may wish to spend a few minutes planning before you start writing.
Do not spend longer than five minutes planning.
Ask the adult to remind you when there is 5 minutes of writing time left.

Instructions for the Spelling Test

The Spelling Test should take about 10 minutes. It is not a timed test.
Before you start the test, ask an adult to cut out page 33 from this book.

You will find your part of the Spelling Test on pages 22 and 23. This is where you write down your answers. When you are ready to start the test, ask the adult to read aloud the complete passage from page 33. Follow and listen carefully – do not write anything yet.

The adult will then read the passage again. This time, he or she will pause so that you can write in the correct spelling of the missing words. Write them down in the gaps on pages 22 and 23. Make sure your writing is clear. If you make a mistake, cross it out and write the word again clearly.

DO NOT TURN OVER THIS PAGE UNTIL YOU ARE READY TO START THE WRITING TEST *LONGER TASK*.

Writing Test
Longer Task:
Instructions and Planning

Ask an adult to read this paper with you before you start the test. The adult is not allowed to help you with the writing, but he or she can make sure that you understand what you have to do.

You will have **45 minutes** for your longer piece of writing, including up to **10 minutes** planning time. You may start your writing as soon as you have finished planning.

The Decision

Here is the outline of a story about a character called Charlie.

One day Charlie, the main character in the story, goes to meet a friend.

Charlie sees this friend doing something wrong – something that might get the friend into serious trouble.

Charlie has to decide what to do.

What should Charlie do?

How will Charlie's friend react?

What happens next?

Your task is to write a story about what Charlie sees and what happens next. You must decide how the story ends.

You will need to think about:
- who the two main characters are and what they are like
- what the incident is and the possible consequences
- what Charlie decides to do
- how the characters react to the events.

EXPLAINING THE UNEXPLAINED?

CONTENTS

INTRODUCTION

Everyone loves a mystery. Things that cannot easily be explained are fascinating and make us ask lots of questions.

Of course, some people like to have an answer to every puzzle and find an explanation for every strange event.

In this booklet, you will read about some mysterious events and things that are difficult to explain. You will also read about some possible explanations – but can they explain everything?

Camilla

by Adèle Geras

An interview with Monica Bridges
(author *of Ghoulies and Ghosties* and *Shades of Darkness*)

by Lynn Michael

In this interview, Monica Bridges has been describing how she grew up in North Borneo, a country on the other side of the world. She has talked about the island, about her school there and about her teacher, Mrs Ashton. She has just described how she and her friend Sarah used to watch Mrs Ashton and her husband Brian arriving at school each morning.

The interview continues…

L.M: Was Sarah your best friend?

M.B: I suppose so. I think so. Certainly she was my everyday, bread-and-butter sort of friend. Our parents did a lot of things together, so we saw a lot of one another. I liked her. I really did like her. I suppose she was my best friend, certainly until Camilla came.

[At this point there is a long silence on the tape …]

M.B: I'm sorry … I'm being silly. It's only that I haven't spoken about Camilla for years. I've thought of her. Maybe what happened all those years ago has turned me into the kind of writer I am.

L.M: Would you mind telling me about it?

M.B: No, I don't think I mind. I've never really told anyone before. I don't know why I've never written about it. Have you got enough tape on this machine? Well then … Camilla.

From the very first time I saw her, I wanted passionately to be her best friend. Camilla was beautiful. She had long, dark hair in plaits and wide grey eyes. There was nothing particularly remarkable about her clothes, and yet she always made the rest of us feel like scarecrows. It wasn't just her looks, though. She was peaceful, somewhere deep inside herself, and you felt, you just knew, that being her friend would be the best thing that could ever happen to you.

She wasn't unfriendly. You mustn't think that. She was always very nice to me, and to Sarah and the other big girls, but she would not, whatever I did, commit herself. She would never say, 'I'll be your best friend.' Do you still have best friends nowadays? In my childhood, your best friend was the most important thing in your life. I was quite shameless in my pursuit of Camilla. I used to pass her notes during lessons, but she never answered. She would smile, and nod her head towards Mrs Ashton as if to say: 'Watch out. Teacher will see you.'

Then it was my tenth birthday. I'd persuaded my parents to have a fancy dress party to which all my friends would come. I arrived at school carrying the invitations and handed them out with some pride. At breaktime, sitting on the steps of the school hut with Camilla, I said:

'You will come, won't you? It'll be such fun. It's on Sunday afternoon.'

Camilla shook her head. 'Oh, Monica, I'm sorry. I have to go away on Friday to visit my uncle, who has a rubber plantation up the coast. On Sunday afternoon when you're having your party, we'll be driving back. I wish I could come.'

'Why don't you try?' I said. 'Try asking your parents to leave a bit earlier, so that you can get there for a while, at least.'

Camilla looked at me very hard then. I haven't forgotten her look, even after forty odd years. I shivered then in spite of the sun burning down on me, and I'm shivering now as I tell you. Camilla said: 'I'll try. I'll try and come.'

[There is a long pause on the tape here. L.M.]

L.M: Did she come? To your party, I mean?

M.B: Oh, yes, she came. We recognized her in spite of her fancy dress. She came as a dragon, wearing a huge elaborate Chinese dragon-mask over her head, so that unless you knew Camilla very well, you would never guess. We knew it was her by the way she walked, but I don't think anyone else noticed that she was wearing her bracelet. She always wore it on her left wrist. It was an identity disc with her name engraved on it. I welcomed her at the door and said: 'Oh, Camilla, I'm so glad you came after all. We're having a lovely party.'

And it was a lovely party. I don't think I've ever had a better birthday. The food was delicious, the games were fun and I won a lot of them, all my presents were wonderful, and best of all, better than anything, Camilla said them at last, the words I wanted to hear more than anything. Everyone else had gone off on a treasure hunt round the garden and we were standing on the verandah together.

'Monica, listen,' she said, 'you've asked me and asked me, and I've never said anything, but I would have liked to be your best friend. I really would. I want you to know that, whatever happens. Do you promise?'

'I promise,' I answered, and she said:

'I haven't got a proper present for you, but you can have my bracelet.' She took it off and fastened it round my wrist.

'But, Camilla,' I said, 'you always wear that … you can't give it to me. It's got your name on it and everything.'

'I don't need it …' Camilla started to say, and then my mother came out and bustled us towards the table where my birthday cake was standing ready to be cut.

The next day, it was school again. I couldn't wait to get there, to take up my new position as Camilla's official best friend. Sarah and I waited behind the frangipani tree for Mrs Ashton, giggling as we thought of the early-morning kiss, and wondering what our teacher would be wearing. Mrs Ashton didn't kiss Brian. It was the first time she had ever left the car without looking fondly behind her.

'They must have had a fight,' Sarah said knowledgeably. 'Her eyes are all red. She's been crying.'

I said nothing. I don't think I knew that grown-ups could cry.

When we had sat down for the first lesson, Mrs Ashton stood up.

'Children,' she said and her voice was thick with tears, 'I have some very sad news for all of you. Camilla won't be coming back … there was a terrible accident yesterday afternoon at about 2.00. Camilla and her parents were driving home and …' Mrs Ashton swallowed. 'They must have been going very fast. The car went off the road. They were killed at once. I'm sure,' Mrs Ashton added, 'that it happened far too quickly for them to have known anything about it. They can't possibly have suffered.'

She sat down suddenly and put her face in her hands. We all sat and stared at one another. I felt … I don't know what I felt except cold, very cold. Then I thought: there must have been a mistake. Camilla was at my party at 3.30 so how could she have died at 2.00? I turned to Sarah. She knew the truth.

'Sarah,' I began.

'Yes?' Tears stood in her eyes.

'Sarah, did you see the person in the Chinese dragon-mask at my party?'

'Yes,' said Sarah. 'I wonder who it can have been. I was sure it was Camilla, but it can't have been, can it?' Sarah burst into tears, and I said nothing. I've never said anything about it to anyone, till now. No one would have believed me.

L.M: Thank you so much for telling me. I'm sorry about your friend. Can you tell me how long ago this was?

M.B: This happened in 1953. I can see by your face that you think writing all these ghost stories has addled my brain. You're being polite, but I don't think you quite believe that Camilla came back from the dead with the gift of her friendship. Am I right?

L.M: No, I do believe you. Truly.

M.B: I think you do … isn't that amazing? And you will be rewarded for your belief. I'll show you the proof.

L.M: Is there proof?

M.B: I've never shown anyone before.

[There's the sound of M.B. opening a locked drawer in her desk. L.M.]

There. Tell me what you see.

L.M: It's a silver bracelet. There's an identity disc on it, engraved with the name: Camilla.

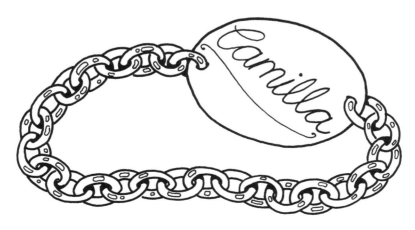

RUINS

Through the mists stand stumps of stone,
Jagged walls with eyeless openings,
Crumbling towers melting in the drizzle,
Rubble merging with the grassy floor.
All that is left – it is no more.

But perhaps that's a figure in the greyness?
A cry being carried on the wind?
Are eyes watching in the half-light?
Are they waiting for us to leave?
   To leave them alone –
        alone,
           all alone
               once
                   more.

GHOSTS
– fact or fiction?

Everyone loves a ghost story. Floating figures in dark corridors, the rattling of chains and things that go bump in the night! Some of these stories are in fact based on real life experiences – although perhaps a little exaggerated to make the story more interesting.

Hundreds of people report seeing ghosts every year, hundreds more experience strange events or hear unexplained sounds. Some of these witnesses are able to describe what they saw or heard in great detail. They are certain that what they witnessed was a ghost.

But despite the hundreds of sightings every year, not everybody believes that ghosts exist. Some people say that these reports are either a deliberate hoax made up by people wanting attention, or else they can be explained by perfectly normal events.

What are ghosts?

Spirits of people who died violently: they cannot rest until they take their revenge?

Friendly spirits who come back to warn or watch over the living?

Spirits who are unaware that they have died: they go about their normal business as if still alive?

Glimpses of the past that only appear when the past and present become confused?

ROCKENHAM TOWER

You enter a small dark chamber lit only by burning candles. In the middle of the wood panelled room is a four-posted bed. The room is unchanged since 1602, when Sir Richard Fawkes was violently murdered in his sleep. Suddenly there is a chilling scream. You turn – and find the ghostly face of Sir Richard staring back at you!

Dare to visit Rockenham Tower?

Exploring the evidence

Sightings

Many people claim to have seen ghostly apparitions. Perhaps the most famous ghost is that of Abraham Lincoln who was president of the USA from 1861 to 1865. His ghost has often been seen walking the corridors of the White House, keeping a watchful eye on what is going on.

Strange happenings

Some reports describe objects being moved or even thrown around. This sort of ghost is called a poltergeist (the word means noisy spirit) and is often malicious.

In Norwood, London, in 1957, the Greenfield family experienced a poltergeist. Furniture floated in the air and hurtled around the bedroom of their young daughter. The family were terrified.

Crisis apparitions

Some ghosts appear only once, at the very moment when the person dies. They appear to a close friend or relation, even though that person is in a completely different place.

In 1893, the ghost of Admiral Sir George Tryon appeared at a party held by his wife in Belgravia, London at the very moment his ship sank in the Mediterranean. He appeared to be completely solid and real, not at all ghost-like.

Sounds

Not all ghosts are seen. Sometimes people hear strange sounds such as bumps, creaks or groans. The George and Dragon Inn in Chester is believed to be haunted by the ghost of a Roman soldier. His footsteps are heard pacing backwards and forwards along an upstairs corridor, as if he were still on duty.

Photographs

Other ghosts only seem to appear when photographs are developed. One of the most famous ghost photographs was taken at Raynham Hall in Norfolk in 1936. It shows a tall shadowy figure standing at the bottom of the wooden staircase. The figure became known as the Brown Lady of Raynham.

What do scientists say?

Most scientists say that ghosts do not exist. It is impossible for objects to vanish and then reappear. Instead, they claim that most 'ghosts' can be explained by perfectly normal events.

- **Just an illusion** – some 'ghosts' are just shadows, mists or strange lighting effects that startle people into believing that they have seen something else.

- **Fakes and forgeries** – photographs of 'ghosts' are easy to fake using computers, or even just by taking two photographs, one on top of another.

- **Noises of nature** – many strange noises are caused by the weather. Even changes in temperature cause materials like wood and metal to expand and contract. This can create all sorts of strange creaks and groans.

- **All in your mind** – the human brain likes to recognise shapes. It will take information from the eyes and turn it into something recognisable such as a figure or face.

- **On the move** – natural ground movements as well as vibrations caused by traffic or heavy machinery can cause objects to move.

Scientists say: *If ghosts really exist, where is the proof?*

What do you think?

Do GHOSTS exist?

Can we be sure?

F.D. Roosevelt once said:

I think it is unwise to say you do not believe in anything when you can't prove that it is either true or untrue.

This Reading Booklet is a pull-out section from
the **Schofield & Sims English Key Stage 2
Practice Papers.**

It is designed as reference material for the Reading Test.

If you are going to try the Reading Test under test
conditions, **do not** read this booklet before the test
session starts.

Published by Schofield and Sims Ltd
Dogley Mill
Fenay Bridge
Huddersfield HD8 0NQ, UK
Tel 01484 607080

www.schofieldandsims.co.uk

First published in 2004
Eighth impression 2010
Copyright © Schofield and Sims Ltd 2004

Author: Carol Matchett

Carol Matchett has asserted her moral right under the
Copyright, Designs and Patents Act, 1988, to be
identified as the author of this work.

The story **Camilla** (see extract on pages 3 to 7) is by
Adèle Geras, and is taken from the Oxford Book of Scary
Tales (Oxford University Press, 1992). **Camilla** is
copyright © Adèle Geras 1991. Permission granted by the
Author.

British Library Cataloguing in Publication Data
A catalogue record for this book is available from the
British Library.

Edited by Carolyn Richardson Publishing Services
(cr@publiserve.co.uk)
Designed by Oxford Designers & Illustrators
Printed in the UK by Wyndeham Gait Ltd,
Grimsby, North East Lincolnshire

ISBN 978 07217 0956 7

Schofield&Sims

Planning

Plan your story under these headings:

The characters in the story	Where and when the story takes place

How the story begins

The main events that happen

How the story ends

Start writing your story on a separate piece of paper as soon as you have finished planning.

This is the end of the Writing Test *Longer Task*.

DO NOT TURN OVER THIS PAGE UNTIL YOU ARE READY TO START THE WRITING TEST *SHORTER TASK*.

Writing Test
Shorter Task

**Ask an adult to read this paper with you before you start the test.
The adult is not allowed to help you with the writing, but he or she can
make sure that you understand what you have to do.**

You will have **20 minutes** to write your shorter piece of writing in this booklet.

Swimming pool closure

You read in the local newspaper that Redcot Community Pool, the swimming pool
near where you live, is about to be closed. People will be expected to travel 10
miles to the next nearest pool.

**Write a short, formal letter to the editor of the newspaper Redcot Times,
protesting about the closure of the pool.**

To get your letter published in the newspaper, it should be short and to the point.
The newspaper will not publish letters that are too long.

You will need to think about:

- the problems caused by closing the pool
- the arguments for why the pool should remain open
- how to put your point of view across
- how to express your ideas clearly in a few words.

Before you start, make some brief notes:

Problems caused by closing Redcot Community Pool:

Why the pool should remain open:

Use this page for your letter.

Swimming pool closure

This is how your letter will appear in the newspaper.

Swimming pool closure – one reader's response

Dear Sir

_____

_____

_____

_____

_____

_____

_____

_____

_____

_____

_____

_____

_____

_____

This is the end of the Writing Test *Shorter Task*.

Writing Test
Shorter Task **score**
Write this score in
the box on page 3

**DO NOT TURN OVER THIS PAGE UNTIL YOU ARE READY
TO START THE SPELLING TEST.**

Spelling Test

The adult who is helping you will read out the passage to you, using the cut-out page 33. Listen carefully.

Ghost hunters

Ghost hunters are scientists who _____ possible hauntings.

People who _____ they have seen a ghost contact them and ask for

their help.

On _____ their first task is to interview the witnesses.

This is very _____ . As there is likely to be no

_____ evidence, the ghost hunters need to

find out _____ what was seen or heard.

The ghost hunters will then carry out a very thorough _____

of the place where the sighting _____ . They will draw a

careful plan of the room, taking _____ measurements and

marking the positions of windows and mirrors.

The first rule of ghost hunting is: appearances can be _____ .

Schofield&Sims
English Key Stage 2
Practice Papers

Revision Guide links
If you need help after your test has been marked, read the following pages in the Revision Guide:
Breaking words into syllables page 80; **Finding hidden letters** page 80; **Is it ie or ei?** page 83;
Is it a soft c or s? page 84; **Adding suffixes** page 81; **Is it a soft g or j?** page 84

To further their _____ the ghost hunters might wish to spend

some time at the site, hoping to see the ghost.

This involves careful _____ and a great deal of

_____. They must keep with them at all times a sound

recorder and a _____ camera to record any strange events.

Having collected all their information they will use books and old maps to

research the _____ of the site.

Only when _____ that they have all the evidence do the

ghost hunters try to explain the _____ events. They will

then _____ their final report.

_____ sightings are explained by perfectly

_____ events.

Total number of words
spelled correctly

*Use page 34 to
convert this total into
the Spelling Test score*

**Spelling Test
total score**
Write this score in
the box on page 3

This is the end of the Spelling Test.

Schofield&Sims
English Key Stage 2
Practice Papers

Revision Guide links
If you need help after your test has been marked, read the following pages in the Revision Guide:
Words with the letter 'q' page 83; **Adding -ed or -ing** page 82; **Making plurals** page 82

Reading Test answers and mark schemes

SECTION 1

Question no.	Correct answer	Marks
1.	Lynn Michael.	1 mark
2.	over 40 years ago. See pages 4 (*I haven't forgotten her look, even after forty odd years*) and 7 (*This happened in 1953*).	1 mark
3.	Sunday afternoon.	1 mark
4.	Their friendship was ordinary and everyday. They did ordinary everyday things together, e.g. *they went to school together, she was someone to play with, talk to.*	1 mark
5.	Answers should refer to any two of the following points: • She was beautiful and elegant. • She seemed different to the other girls. • She seemed special and Monica was intrigued/ fascinated by her. • She was peaceful and calm.	max. 2 marks
6.	Answers should refer to what Monica Bridges is likely to be thinking about at this time, e.g. *She is thinking about Camilla and remembering what happened; She is deciding whether to tell the story of Camilla.*	1 mark
7.	The correct numbering is: 3 Camilla gives Monica her bracelet. 2 Camilla says she will not be able to come to Monica's party. 5 Monica shows Lynn Michael a bracelet engraved with the name Camilla. 4 Mrs Ashton tells the class about Camilla's death. Give 2 marks for all 4 correctly numbered. Give 1 mark for 2 or 3 correctly numbered.	max. 2 marks
8.	Answers should refer to any of the following points: • The pauses in the interview. • Details such as the description of the look from Camilla that made Monica shiver. • The comments made by Monica, e.g. about not having told anyone before. • The strange things that Camilla says to Monica at the party, e.g. not needing the bracelet any more. • The unusual events the next morning when Mrs Ashton arrives at school.	max. 3 marks
9.	Answers should refer to the mixture of feelings felt by Monica at this point – shock at hearing about her friend's death and confusion because she had seen Camilla at her party after the time she was supposed to have died.	1 mark
10.	She writes ghost stories and it might have been this experience that first inspired her to write or gave her an interest in ghosts.	1 mark
11.	From Monica Bridges' point of view.	1 mark
12.	Answers should refer to typical features of the ghost story genre that are not present in this story, or unusual features of this story. Marks can be given for any of the following points: • Ghost stories usually have dark, spooky settings. • This story is more realistic than most ghost stories. • The characters are not typical – e.g., the ghost is friendly. • The mood of the story – e.g., this story is more mysterious than scary. • Untypical events – e.g., the main character not being aware of the ghost until later; the main character is not scared of the ghost. • This story is written in the form of an interview.	max. 3 marks

Question no.	Correct answer	Marks
13.	No marks are given for ticking the yes/no boxes. Give marks for the reasons given to support the choice. Answers might refer to aspects of the plot, the characters, the genre of the story or how the story is told: • Give 1 mark for answers giving a reason that is appropriate to the story. • Give 2 marks for answers that explain the reason by referring to specific aspects of the text or giving a specific example from the story. • Give 3 marks for answers that include more than one point and support these points with appropriate references to the text.	max. 3 marks

SECTION 2

Question no.	Correct answer	Marks
14.	Give 1 mark for any **two** of the following… • *(Through the) mists* • *(melting in the) drizzle* • *greyness* • *carried on the wind* • *half-light*	1 mark
15.	a) The first verse describes the actual ruins of the castle; the second verse imagines ghosts of people who lived there. Accept also answers that say the first verse is real, but the second verse is imagined.	1 mark
	b) Accept answers that refer to how the lines in the second verse are a series of questions, **or** answers that refer to the change in the wording and/or layout of the last line of the second verse.	1 mark
16.	a) the windows	1 mark
	b) The windows are no longer used, no-one looks out of them any more.	1 mark

SECTION 3

Question no.	Correct answer	Marks
17.	a) Answers should refer to the number of witnesses or the fact that lots of people see or hear ghosts every year.	1 mark
	b) Some people say that sightings are a deliberate hoax **or** some people believe the sightings can be explained by natural causes (only 1 reason needs to be given).	1 mark
18.	to persuade the reader	1 mark
19.	Give 1 mark for any of the following points (up to a maximum of 2): • Describing the scene (e.g. *small dark chamber*) • Making the reader picture him/herself there (*You enter…*) • Build-up of details (Details about the room, the bed, Sir Richard's murder…) • Choice of words and phrases (e.g. *chilling scream*) • Exclamation (you *find the ghostly face…!*) • Question to the reader (*Dare to visit Rockenham Tower?*) Do not give marks just for words and phrases copied from the text. There must be some explanation.	max. 2 marks
20.	Answers should refer to the purpose of sub-headings, e.g.: • They show the different types of evidence described on the page. • If you look at the page quickly, they give you an idea of the different sorts of evidence. • They could help you to find information about a particular sort of evidence quickly.	1 mark
21.	Give one mark for each row completed correctly (no half marks allowed):	
	The White House / Seen (often) / Abraham Lincoln	1 mark
	The George and Dragon Inn, Chester / Heard (strange sounds) / A Roman soldier	1 mark
	Belgravia, London / Seen (solid and real) / Admiral Sir George Tryon	1 mark

Question no.	Correct answer	Marks
22.	a) The poltergeist/The ghost at the Greenfield's house/The ghost in Norwood	1 mark
	b) Any of the following reasons can be given a mark: <ul><li>It says this sort of ghost is often malicious.</li><li>It threw furniture around the room.</li><li>It says the family were terrified.</li></ul>	1 mark
23.	Answers should link to the theme of the information given on that page. Any of the following can be given a mark: <ul><li>Because the scientists don't really think they are ghosts.</li><li>Because they might not be ghosts at all.</li><li>Because the information on this page gives other reasons for what happens.</li></ul>	1 mark
24.	Answers should refer to why a bullet point list and/or bold print has been used, e.g.: <ul><li>It separates out each idea clearly.</li><li>It makes it easier to read than if all of the ideas were joined together.</li><li>The words in bold print give you the main points in a short, eye-catching form.</li></ul>	1 mark
25.	Give **1 mark** for a simple answer that refers to the weather causing strange noises. Give **2 marks** for more detailed answers that explain that this particular ghost is in a building and changes in temperature could make some of the building materials creak as they expand or contract.	max. 2 marks
26.	The questions encourage the reader to think about the information given in all parts of the article and to decide what they think.	1 mark
27.	Answers should make links between the quotation and the information given in the article, e.g.: <ul><li>It makes you think about which ideas can be proved and which cannot.</li><li>It gives you someone's opinion on ghosts.</li><li>It's the opposite view to that of the scientists.</li></ul>	1 mark
28.	a) We do not know for certain if ghosts exist.	1 mark
	b) Give 1 mark each for any two reasons that refer to an aspect of the text, e.g.: <ul><li>The title sets the question of 'Ghosts – fact or fiction?'</li><li>The article describes evidence for ghosts really existing in 'Exploring the evidence', but gives the opposite view in 'What do scientists say?'</li><li>The introduction gives both views.</li><li>There are lots of questions.</li></ul>	max. 2 marks

SECTION 4

29.	Give 1 mark each for any two of the following points: <ul><li>They appeared at the moment when the person died.</li><li>They appeared to someone they were close to.</li><li>They appeared in a different place to where they died.</li><li>They both seemed to be completely solid and real.</li></ul>	max. 2 marks
30.	Give 1 mark each for any two answers recognising that the theme of the booklet is whether ghostly happenings can be explained or not, e.g.: <ul><li>The title has been chosen because it describes some strange events and some of them can be explained and some cannot.</li></ul> Give 2 marks for answers that recognise the theme and refer specifically to the story and/or information text in the booklet.	max. 2 marks

Write the total Reading Test score in the boxes on pages 3 and 16.

Revision Guide links
If the test results show that the child needs help, refer to the following pages in the separate Revision Guide – for help with individual questions, see the pages referred to at the foot of each page of the Reading Test:
Reading stories pages 4–15; **Reading poetry** pages 16–22; **Reading non-fiction** pages 23–33

Writing Test mark schemes

Longer Task

There are no right and wrong answers to this Writing Test, but different aspects of the child's writing are assessed. The focus is on three particular aspects:

- Sentence structure and punctuation
- Text structure and organisation
- Composition and effectiveness of the writing ('effect').

Up to three additional marks will be given for handwriting (see below).

Using the mark schemes

Read the mark scheme for **Sentence structure and punctuation**. Choose the **one** set of statements that seem to best describe the writing. Tick the appropriate box and give a mark within the range shown.

Read the mark scheme for **Text structure and organisation**. Choose the **one** set of statements that seem to best describe the writing. Tick the appropriate box and give a mark within the range shown.

Read the mark scheme for **Composition and effect**. Choose the **one** set of statements that seem to best describe the writing. Tick the appropriate box and give a mark within the range shown.

Finally, mark the **handwriting**. Three broad descriptions of handwriting style are given in the table below. Choose the **one** description that best describes the child's handwriting in the *Longer Task*. Write the mark in the column beside it.

Handwriting description	Marks given	Marks available
Most upper and lower case letters are formed correctly, but size and spacing may be uneven. Some of the letters are joined up.		1 mark
Writing is joined up, with letters correctly formed and mostly the right size. Letters and words are properly spaced.		2 marks
Handwriting is joined and looks fluent and flowing.		3 marks

Total score for Handwriting

Add the marks, as explained on page 30, to find the total score for the *Longer Task*. Write the total score for the Writing Test *Longer Task* in the boxes on pages 3 and 30.

Shorter Task

There are no right and wrong answers to this Writing Test but, as in the *Longer Task*, different aspects of the child's writing are assessed. The focus this time is on two particular aspects:

- Sentence structure, punctuation and text organisation
- Composition and effectiveness of the writing ('effect').

Using the mark schemes

Read the mark scheme for **Sentence structure, punctuation and text organisation**. Choose the set of statements that seem to best describe the child's writing. Tick the appropriate box and give the marks shown.

Read the mark scheme for **Composition and effect**. Choose the set of statements that seem to best describe the child's writing. Tick the appropriate box and give the marks shown. Total up the marks to find the total score for the *Shorter Task*. Write the total score for the Writing Test *Shorter Task* in the boxes on pages 3 and 21.

Please note: the mark scheme for the Spelling Test appears on page 34.

Writing Test *Longer Task* mark schemes

Sentence structure and punctuation

Description	Marks given	Marks available
Nearly all short simple sentences (often starting with name/pronoun + verb). Any longer sentences tend to use the words *and, but, so*. Sentences sometimes start with capital letters and end with full stops.		1 mark
There are some longer sentences using simple connectives such as *but, so, then, or*. Verbs are often simple and repeated, e.g. *went, said, had*. Some sentences include simple adjectives or adverbs. Subject and verb usually agree (e.g. *I was; he/she was; they were*). Most sentences are correctly punctuated using capital letters, full stops, and question marks; commas in lists. Speech marks may be used.		2–3 marks
There are some complex sentences using a range of sentence connectives (e.g. *if, while, until, although*). Different types of sentences are used in dialogue (e.g. exclamations and questions). Adjectives and adverbs are used to extend ideas and add interest to sentences. Pronouns are used properly (e.g. does not swap from *he* to *she* or to *I*). Tense is appropriate and consistent (e.g. the story is told in past tense). Sentences are correctly punctuated and commas are sometimes used to separate parts of a sentence. Speech marks are used to mark direct speech.		4–5 marks
Simple and complex sentences are used effectively in the story. Some sentence structures are chosen for effect, e.g. starting with a subordinate clause; short sentences for impact. Phrases are extended to add detail; adverbs indicate attitudes, e.g. *unfortunately at that moment…* Almost all sentences are correctly punctuated, including the use of some more sophisticated punctuation marks, e.g. dashes or brackets.		6–7 marks
Sentence structures and sentence types are used to create a range of effects, e.g. starting with a subordinate clause; short sentences for impact; questions and exclamations for effect. A range of punctuation is used correctly. Punctuation is also used to vary the pace of the story, e.g. through use of dash, semi-colon.		8 marks

Marks for **Sentence structure and punctuation** [ ]

Tick only **one** of the boxes in this column. Give the number of marks that you think is appropriate, within the range of **Marks available**.

Revision Guide links
If the test results show that the child needs help, refer to the following pages in the separate Revision Guide:
Varying sentence types page 70; **Punctuating sentences** pages 69, 74, 75; **Forming complex sentences** pages 71–73; **Commas** page 76; **Using pronouns** page 67; **Speech marks** page 45; **Adjectives and adverbs** pages 65, 66; **More complex punctuation** pages 77–78

Text structure and organisation

Description	Marks given	Marks available
Has some features of a story, e.g. a conventional opening such as *One day...* Ideas are grouped into a series of sentences that may seem like a string of events. The words *and*, *then* are used often to link events. The use of first or third person may not be consistent.		1 mark
The story has a beginning, middle and simple ending. Some of these parts may be marked by paragraphs. The story may not be well-paced, e.g. too long spent on the early events; a rushed ending. The events are in a chronological sequence with time-related phrases used to link the events, e.g. *Suddenly... Later...* Pronouns help to make connections between sentences.		2–3 marks
The story has a beginning, middle and clear ending. The main events in the story are logically linked and easy to follow. Paragraphs are used to make clear the sequence of events (e.g. new paragraph started for a new event, or when the story moves on in time or place). Connecting words and phrases are used to indicate movements in place as well as time (e.g. *Meanwhile back at school...*) Each movement gives rise to a new series of events.		4–5 marks
Well structured with interesting opening, series of events and a convincing ending that develops out of the main plot. Paragraphs mark the main divisions in the story (e.g. main events). The structure and order of the paragraphs help to shape the story, e.g. building up to a climax. The writer is able to move the story forward effectively and at an appropriate pace. References to the characters are varied to avoid repetition.		6–7 marks
Well constructed, handling a more complex series of events. Interesting links between events, e.g. an early event becomes significant later. Uses devices such as flashbacks or shifts in time or point of view. Each paragraph has a clear focus and takes the story forward at an appropriate pace.		8 marks

Marks for **Text structure and organisation**

please turn over

Revision Guide links
If the test results show that the child needs help, refer to the following pages in the separate Revision Guide:
Developing ideas pages 34, 35; **Ending stories** page 42; **Linking events** page 37;
Using paragraphs page 38; **Starting stories** page 39; **Connecting events** pages 38, 68

Composition and effect

Description	Marks given	Marks available
A simple story based on the prompt. Sticks to the main events – not much development. Some detail to interest the reader, e.g. simple description of a character.		1–2 marks
Develops the main idea given in the task. There is some detail included to interest the reader, e.g. description of characters or events; some dialogue between characters. Some evidence of viewpoint, e.g. comments on feelings or motives of the main characters (e.g. *Charlie looked worried*). Some words or phrases chosen for effect, e.g. description, or amusing dialogue.		3–5 marks
Takes the ideas in the task and creates a story about the situation with enough detail to hold the reader's attention (e.g. developing the characters and their relationship through relevant dialogue, details about actions, feelings). There is a sense of the author's viewpoint, such as seeing the events from a point of view of the main character (e.g. *Charlie watched with growing concern*). Some more adventurous words and phrases are chosen for effect. Style fits with the type of story (realistic fiction).		6–8 marks
Develops a story around the issue/ dilemma introduced in the task, using a combination of dialogue, description and action. Characters are developed and made believable – behaviour and dialogue fits with description of the character; feelings are implied. Uses writer techniques to capture and keep the interest of the reader, e.g. starting in an interesting way; commenting on events, addressing the reader. Narrative voice (e.g. comments to the reader) and style are appropriate to the form of the story (realistic narrative). Vocabulary is chosen for interest and impact. May use non-standard English in dialogue to fit with the type of story (realistic).		9–11 marks
From the task, develops the theme of the story (helping a friend; doing what's right) as well as describing what happens. May include some conflict between the characters or changes in their relationship during the course of the story. Definite sense of narrative voice – uses a range of narrative devices to comment on the events. Creates moments of tension, excitement. May include language effects such as figurative language or alliteration.		12 marks

Marks for **Composition and effect** ☐

Now add together the marks for:
Handwriting, *page 27,*
Sentence structure and punctuation, *page 28,*
Text structure and organisation, *page 29,*
and **Composition and effect** *(above)*

Total score for Writing Test *Longer Task* ☐
Write this score in the box on page 3

Revision Guide links
If the test results show that the child needs help, refer to pages 34–47 of the separate Revision Guide and read carefully the following pages:
Using dialogue pages 44, 45; **Developing settings** page 41; **Using description** page 43; **Creating effects, e.g. suspense** page 47; **Creating characters** page 40; **Narrative voice** page 46

Writing Test *Shorter Task* mark schemes

Sentence structure, punctuation and text organisation

Description	Marks given	Marks available
Mainly simple sentences. Many sentences may start in the same way, e.g. *The pool is...* Connectives, when used, are fairly simple, e.g. *and, then, but.* Shows some organisation of ideas, but points are more like a list. Pronouns are used to link ideas between sentences, e.g. *The pool/It.* Sentences sometimes have full stops and capital letters.		1 mark
Some connectives, such as *so, if, also, but,* are used to link ideas in sentences. Some repetition in how sentences start, e.g. *The pool was...; It has...* Adjectives and adverbs are sometimes used to emphasise points, e.g. *This would be a very bad idea.* Includes a brief opening or concluding statement. Full stops (or question/exclamation marks) and capital letters are correctly used most of the time; commas are used in lists.		2 marks
Some complex sentences are used to explain or develop ideas, e.g. giving reasons; showing results. Connectives are used to explain, order or for emphasis, e.g. *If... then...; when; __ means that...* Sentence constructions varied by using adverb phrases. Verbs varied to indicate possible events, future events, past events. Ideas developed in paragraphs – topic sentences are used to introduce the main points in the letter. Points may be linked by phrases such as *Firstly, Lastly.* Most sentences are correctly punctuated. Within sentences, commas mark phrases or clauses.		3 marks
Includes a range of compound and complex sentences with varied connectives. Variety of sentence structures for purpose and effect, e.g. short sentences or exclamations for impact; complex sentences to develop ideas. Adjective/adverb phrases add variety and precision. Organised in paragraphs with emphasis on the main ideas. Almost all sentences are correctly punctuated, including more complex punctuation, e.g. brackets, colons, semi-colons.		4 marks

Marks for **Sentence structure, punctuation and text organisation** [ ]

please turn over

Schofield&Sims
English Key Stage 2
Practice Papers

Revision Guide links
If the test results show that the child needs help, refer to the following pages in the separate Revision Guide:
Varying sentence types page 70; **Writing letters** page 55; **Forming complex sentences** pages 71–73; **Punctuating sentences** pages 69, 74, 75; **Using connectives** page 68; **Commas** page 76; **Writing paragraphs** pages 52, 53; **More complex punctuation** pages 77–78

Composition and effect

Description	Marks given	Marks available
Mostly a series of statements. Ideas not really developed. May include irrelevant material (e.g. long description of the pool). The purpose of the letter (to protest/put a point of view) might be shown at the start and end of the letter but becomes lost in the rest of the letter. Some detail to interest the reader (e.g. *The pool is great*). Sounds like spoken language, not formal.		1 mark
Develops one or two ideas suggested by the task (e.g. the fact that it is a long way to travel to the other pool). Probably uneven with some points covered in too much detail and others too briefly. There are some signs of the writer's purpose/point of view, e.g. in attempts to protest, explain, give a point of view, persuade the reader. Some attempts at a more formal style, e.g. making points less personal (*Lots of people think...*). Vocabulary sometimes specific, but sometimes vague (*lots of things*).		2–3 marks
Picks up on the main points in the task, e.g. protesting, explaining problems, arguing for the pool to stay open. Attempts to persuade others to agree. Viewpoint is clear, e.g. suggesting the writer's disappointment. Uses some language and stylistic effects to make points more effective, e.g. adjectives, adverbs, questions, exclamations (e.g. *Clearly, this is not right!*) A clear attempt to write in a more formal style, e.g. in the terms used, how points are expressed (e.g. uses formal terms such as *transport problems*).		4–5 marks
Develops some of the ideas from the original prompt in an interesting way. A real sense of expressing the writer's feelings, e.g. disgust at the decision to close the pool; determination that the pool should stay open. Uses stylistic techniques, e.g. in direct appeals to the reader, rhetorical questions. Uses language to make points succinctly and effectively, e.g. carefully chosen nouns, adjectives, verbs (e.g. *improved facilities, outraged, disappointed...*) The letter has an appropriate formal tone to give the message weight.		6–7 marks
Develops ideas from the original prompt in an unusual and original way. There is a real sense of the writer and the writer's purpose throughout the letter. Awareness of the reader is shown in the way that the writing seeks to capture the reader's attention and make him/her agree with the opinion given. Uses a range of stylistic devices to express own point of view effectively. An appropriate level of formality is maintained throughout.		8 marks

Marks for **Composition and effect** ☐

Now add together the marks for:
Sentence structure, punctuation and text organisation, *page 31,*
and **Composition and effect** *(above)*

Total score for Writing Test *Shorter Task* ☐
Write this score in the boxes on pages 3 and 21

Revision Guide links
If the test results show that the child needs help, refer to the following pages in the separate Revision Guide:
Purpose and audience page 49; **Using stylistic effects** pages 62 (32); **Developing ideas** page 51; **Formal writing** pages 56, 57; **Putting a point of view** page 30

Spelling Test

The Spelling Test should take about 10 minutes to complete. It is not a timed test.

Before you start

- Before you start the Spelling Test, cut out this page along the dotted line. This will allow the child taking the test to write his or her answers on pages 22 and 23 of the Practice Papers book.

During the test

- When the child is ready to start the test, make sure that he or she has the Practice Papers book open at pages 22 and 23.
- Tell the child: **I am going to read this passage to you. Listen carefully – do not write anything down yet.**
- Read slowly and clearly.
- Then tell the child: **I am going to read this passage to you a second time. This time, write the missing word in each gap. Try to spell the missing words correctly. Make sure your writing is clear. If you make a mistake, cross it out and write the word again clearly.**
- Read the passage again. This time, leave a pause after each word that appears **underlined in bold**. Give the child time to write the word in the gap, then continue.

Ghost hunters

Ghost hunters are scientists who **investigate** possible hauntings. People who **believe** they have seen a ghost contact them and ask for their help.

On **arrival** their first task is to interview the witnesses. This is very **important**. As there is likely to be no **physical** evidence, the ghost hunters need to find out **exactly** what was seen or heard.

The ghost hunters will then carry out a very thorough **examination** of the place where the sighting **occurred**. They will draw a careful plan of the room, taking **precise** measurements and marking the positions of windows and mirrors.

The first rule of ghost hunting is: appearances can be **deceptive**.

To further their **enquiries** the ghost hunters might wish to spend some time at the site, hoping to see the ghost. This involves careful **planning** and a great deal of **patience**. They must keep with them at all times a sound recorder and a **digital** camera to record any strange events.

Having collected all their information they will use books and old maps to research the **history** of the site.

Only when **satisfied** that they have all the evidence do the ghost hunters try to explain the **mysterious** events. They will then **produce** their final report.

Generally sightings are explained by perfectly **natural** events.

This is the end of the Spelling Test.

After the test

- When the child has finished the Spelling Test, **keep this sheet!**
- You can mark the test using the mark scheme on the back of this page.

Spelling Test mark scheme

After the Spelling Test, check the child's spelling of each word against the words appearing **underlined in bold** in the passage you read aloud (see page 33).

Please note: If the child spells **enquiries** as **inquiries**, you should accept this alternative spelling as correct.

Count the number of words the child spelled correctly.
Then use the table below to work out the child's score for the Spelling Test. For example, if the child spelled a total of 13 words correctly, his or her Spelling Test score would be 5.

Total number of words spelled correctly	Spelling Test score
1 2	1
3 4 5	2
6 7 8	3
9 10 11	4
12 13 14	5
15 16 17	6
18 19 20	7

Words spelled correctly [ ]   **Spelling Test total score** [ ]

Write the Spelling Test total score in the boxes on pages 3 and 23.

What next?

Now that the child has done all three papers within the Writing Test, you can find the overall score for Writing by adding together the following scores:
● Writing Test *Longer Task*
● Writing Test *Shorter Task*
● Spelling Test.

Page 35 tells you how to use this score and the Reading Test score to get some idea of the educational level at which the child is working.

> **Revision Guide links**
> If the test results show that the child needs help, refer to pages 79–85 in the separate Revision Guide and particularly: **Learning to spell** page 79; **More spelling rules** page 83; **Breaking words into syllables** page 80; **Difficult letters** page 84; **Root words, prefixes and suffixes** page 81; **Homophones and other tricky words** page 85; **Verb and plural endings** page 82

How to convert scores to levels

National Curriculum levels measure a child's progress in each subject. Each level is like one step. As children continue their education, they move up through the levels. Children within Key Stage 2 are working at a level somewhere between levels 2 and 5. Schools encourage children to reach level 4 by the end of Key Stage 2 (Year 6, age 10/11).

You can get an idea of the level a child is working at from the total scores that he or she obtains on the practice papers. First, you need to write the child's scores in the boxes below.

Look at the Reading Test box on page 3 and copy the score into the Reading Test score box below. Then look at the three Writing Test scores on page 3 (Writing Test *Longer Task*, Writing Test *Shorter Task* and Spelling Test). Add these three together and write the total in the Writing Test score box below. Finally, add the Reading Test score and the Writing Test score to obtain the Total Key Stage 2 English Practice Papers score. Write it in the third box.

Score   **Level**

Reading Test score   **Reading level**

Writing Test score   **Writing level**
Add together the following scores:
Writing Test *Longer Task*,
Writing Test *Shorter Task* and Spelling Test

Total Key Stage 2 English Practice Papers score   **Overall English level**

Overall level

You can use the chart below to work out the child's overall level. In the National Tests, the number of marks needed to gain a particular level changes each year. Nevertheless, this chart will give you some idea of the approximate level that the child is working at.

Child's total score (maximum 100)	29 or below	30–49	50–72	73+
Level	Level 1/2	Level 3	Level 4	Level 5

Looking separately at reading and writing

These charts will give you an idea of the separate levels that the child may be working at in reading and in writing. Use the two separate scores in the boxes that you filled in above.

Reading

Child's total score in Reading Test (maximum 50)	13 or below	14–24	25–36	37+
Level	Level 1/2	Level 3	Level 4	Level 5

Writing

Child's total score in Writing Test (maximum 50)	13 or below	14–24	25–36	37+
Level	Level 1/2	Level 3	Level 4	Level 5

Please note

The level obtained from the Schofield & Sims Key Stage 2 English Practice Papers is only valid if the child is nearing the end of Key Stage 2 and has done each test under proper test conditions, without reference to the separate Revision Guide or other English materials.

The level obtained is only an *indication* of the level at which the child is working, and it may not match the level given by the child's teacher.

The Schofield & Sims Revision Guides help children to revise for the Key Stage tests (SATs) by guiding them through what they have already learned at school on a topic-by-topic basis. The Guides have been written by teachers and are designed for children to use independently at home or in school. They are comprehensive and provide excellent value for money.

The **Key Stage 2 English Practice Papers** contained in this book are similar in both appearance and content to the actual Key Stage 2 English tests and give children a valuable opportunity to prepare for them. The papers included are:

- Reading Test (accompanied by a Reading Booklet, which is a pull-out from the centre of this book)
- Writing Test *Longer Task*
- Writing Test *Shorter Task*
- Spelling Test

Full instructions and detailed mark schemes are provided, together with tables that give an indication of the level at which the child is working. The papers are cross-referenced to the separate Key Stage 2 English Revision Guide, which children can refer to for help.

Also available:

The full range of Schofield & Sims Revision Guides and Practice Papers is shown here.

At Key Stage 1

Revision Guide	Practice Papers	Revision Guide	Revision Guide
ISBN 978 07217 0951 2	ISBN 978 07217 0952 9	ISBN 978 07217 1121 8	ISBN 978 07217 1120 1

At Key Stage 2

Revision Guide	Practice Papers	Revision Guide	Practice Papers	Revision Guide	Practice Papers
ISBN 978 07217 0953 6	ISBN 978 07217 0954 3	ISBN 978 07217 0955 0	ISBN 978 07217 0956 7	ISBN 978 07217 0957 4	ISBN 978 07217 0958 1

For further information, see **www.schofieldandsims.co.uk** or **telephone 01484 607080**

ISBN 978-07217-0956-7

9 780721 709567

£2.95
(Retail price)
Key Stage 2
Age range: 7–11 years

FSC
Mixed Sources
Product group from well-managed forests and other controlled sources
Cert no. TT-COC-002542
www.fsc.org
© 1996 Forest Stewardship Council